Something is Watching

written by Lucinda Cotter

illustrated by Lesley Danson

"Dad ...," said Nick.

"I think something is watching us."

Nick looked into a large clump
of trees and ferns.

Nick, his dad and his sister
were on a special camping trip.

They were camping in a rainforest.

"This rainforest is
full of different animals," said Dad.

"It's a wonderful place to visit."

Nick couldn't believe all the different trees
and plants around their camp.

"Hey, Dad!" he shouted.

"Look at this huge plant."

"That's a fern," said Dad.
"Ferns are the oldest plants in the world."

"Everyone please stay on the walkway,"
said Pia.
Pia was their guide.
"I don't want anyone to get lost,"
she said.
"The walkway protects the forest floor.
But it also keeps us safe."

"Hey!" Nick jumped.
"Something just hit me on the head!"
He looked up into the trees,
but he couldn't see anything there.

"You're making it up," said Sophie.
"You just want everyone to look at you."

In the afternoon, they stopped
at a water hole for a rest and a snack.

Nick put his apple on a rock
and took off his shoes and socks.
He put his feet into the cool water.
"Ah!" he said, kicking his feet.
"This feels so good."
But when he reached for his apple,
it was gone!
"Who took my apple?" he shouted.

"Don't look at me," said Sophie.
"Maybe you dropped it in the water."

Nick looked around.

He saw a lizard run up a tree.

He watched a bird fly from tree to tree.

He could hear the frogs croaking
in the river.

There were many animals around him,
but he **still** had the feeling
that he was being watched.

On the way back to the camp,
Nick couldn't believe his eyes!
Some people **zoomed** past.
They were high above the trees.
When Nick looked up again,
he saw they were hanging
from a big wire.
The wire went between the trees.

"That wire you can see is called
a zip line," said Pia, pointing up.
"It's a wonderful way to see
the rainforest."

"Maybe they were the ones watching me,"
Nick thought to himself.

Nick was really tired
by the time they got back to camp.
So he went to the tent to get
something to eat and to sit down.

But when he got there,
he heard a sound coming from
inside the tent.
There was something or someone inside!
And it wasn't Dad or Sophie!

When Nick peeked inside the tent,
he couldn't believe it.
Their clothes were all over the place.
So was the food.
The tent was a mess!

Just then Nick saw something move.

It was his hat.

The hat jumped from one side of the tent to the other.

Then it jumped towards him!

The hat jumped out of the tent.

Then something jumped out of the hat!

Nick saw that it was a small monkey.

And it was eating his apple!

Then the monkey ran up a nearby tree
and threw a berry at Nick.

"Dad! Sophie!" shouted Nick.
"I wasn't making it up!
I really **was** being watched!"

"You can say that again!" laughed Dad.